The Maccabee on the Mantel™

By Abra Liberman Garrett and Four Day Weekend
Illustrated by Ivan Escalante

Created by Abra Liberman Garrett and Four Day Weekend
Written by Abra Liberman Garrett
Illustrated by Ivan Escalante
Letters by Tony Garza

Published by Viper Comics
Production by Cosmic Ray Gun
First Edition: October 2013
ISBN 13: 978-1-62098-798-8

Viper Entertainment Inc. Dba Viper Comics
9400 N. MacArthur Blvd. , Suite 124-215
Irving, Texas 75063

Jessie Garza – President and Publisher
Dale Mettam – Editor in Chief
Tony Garza – Creative Director
Jaime Delarosa - Production Director and Assistant Editor

www.MaccabeeOnTheMantel.com
www.FourDayWeekend.com

To Robert, Jackson, and Charley,
who make all of my days a 'Festival of Light'

For all the Jewish children of yesterday, today, and tomorrow,
and the light they bring to our world…
especially Sophia (Tzofiyah) Allenberg

It’s Hanukkah, oh Hanukkah, and this Maccabee has come,
To spend Hanukkah with YOU, so let’s find out where he’s from…

In the land of Jerusalem, long ago and far away
King Antiochus told the Jews, “Hey, you have to pray my way!”

“We refuse,” said the Jews, “And in God’s name we shall fight,
To worship God as we choose, for we know that is our right!”

"Maccabee" means "hammer," and they fought hard and long,
And while their army was much smaller, they were also very strong.

When they finally won the battle, they went on to their temple to pray,
But when it came time to light their menorah, they had oil for just one day.

Yet instead of burning one day, by a great miracle the oil lasted eight.
The Maccabees had won. Their flame stayed lit; there was much to celebrate!

This little Maccabee is here to spend the month of *Kislev* with you,
To help YOU be just like a Maccabee: honest, brave and true.

Now that you've met your Maccabee, give him a name that fits him well.

He may seem to you like an Abraham, or perhaps a Jacob, Saul or Mel.

He will cruise around your house finding a different location each day.

And if the spot he finds is crazy, well, then just laugh and say, "*Oy vey!*"

Your Maccabee can take part as you play the *dreidel* game,
He can join you in the blessing as you light the *shamash* flame.

He'd probably like a *latke* with apple sauce and sour cream
That you and he can eat as you watch the candles gleam.

You can *kibbitz* with your Maccabee, and tell him what’s on your mind;
Because he is your friend, like you, he’s a hero, good and kind.

So enjoy this special time, with your Maccabee around,
For he is here to remind you that miracles abound.

Our Maccabee, Named

First:
Middle:
Last:
Hebrew Name:
Joined our family on this date:____________
Hereby helping us, the __________ family, make our Festival of Lights even brighter.

He will forever serve to remind us that miracles abound.

Hanukkah Blessings

בָּרוּךְ אַתָּה יְיָ אֱלֹהֵינוּ מֶלֶךְ הָעוֹלָם, אֲשֶׁר קִדְּשָׁנוּ בְּמִצְוֹתָיו, וְצִוָּנוּ לְהַדְלִיק נֵר שֶׁל חֲנֻכָּה.

Baruch atah, Adonai Eloheinu, Melech haolam, asher kid'shanu b'mitzvotav v'tsiv-anu l'hadlik ner shel Hanukkah.

Blessed are You, Adonai our God, Sovereign of all, who hallows us with mitzvot, commanding us to kindle the Hanukkah lights.

בָּרוּךְ אַתָּה יְיָ אֱלֹהֵינוּ מֶלֶךְ הָעוֹלָם, שֶׁעָשָׂה נִסִּים לַאֲבוֹתֵינוּ וְאִמּוֹתֵינוּ בַּיָּמִים הָהֵם בַּזְּמַן הַזֶּה.

Baruch atah, Adonai Eloheinu, Melech haolam, she-asah nisim la'avoteinu v'imoteinu bayamim hahaeim baz'man hazeh.

Blessed are You, Adonai our God, Sovereign of all, who performed wonderous deeds for our ancestors in days of old at this season.

For the first night only

בָּרוּךְ אַתָּה יְיָ אֱלֹהֵינוּ מֶלֶךְ הָעוֹלָם, שֶׁהֶחֱיָנוּ וְקִיְּמָנוּ וְהִגִּיעָנוּ לַזְּמַן הַזֶּה.

Baruch atah, Adonai Eloheinu, Melech haolam, shehecheyanu v'kiy'manu v'higianu laz'man hazeh.

Blessed are You, Adonai our God, Sovereign of all, for giving us life, for sustaining us, and for enabling us to reach this season.

Creating Your Own Family Traditions

Now that your little Maccabee has moved in, it is time to really make some memories! There are infinite options to create traditions as unique and special as your own family is, but here are some ideas to get you started.

✡ Magical Maccabees - Some Maccabees are "magical" and they go off by themselves to hide every night (do they fly, do they walk – who knows?) and every morning it is up to the children of the house to discover where their Maccabee has landed.

✡ The Afikomen meets the Maccabee – Other Maccabees are parent operated. Just like the afikomen at Passover, mom and/or dad do the hiding and the kids do the seeking.

✡ Maccabee Scavenger Style – Have a nightly scavenger hunt to find the Maccabee who sits "guarding" that evening's Hanukkah presents.

✡ Turn the Tables - Let the kids hide the Maccabee from their parents. Nothing is more fun for children than the opportunity to outsmart the adults.

✡ Show your love through food - No, really, we mean it! Let that little Maccabee make latkes with your family. Or doughnuts. Or decorate those Hanukkah cookies. When's the last time you cooked with a Maccabee in the Kitchen?

✡ "And when it's dry and ready…" - Dreidel with the Maccabee, because sometimes the sweetest traditions are the oldest ones. Play Dreidel as a family, just like you used to do with yours, but this time include the Maccabee and give him his own gelt.

✡ Set the place aglow - Light the Menorah (the Hanukkiah) with your Maccabee! He can recite the blessings and sing the prayers right along with your family.

✡ Maccabee Mitzvah time – Maccabees and Mitzvot go together like latkes and apple sauce. Nothing is more rewarding for a Maccabee than helping others, so choose a family Mitzvah.

Our **MACCABEE ON THE MANTEL**™ family would love to hear about the traditions your family creates! Please send your ideas and pictures to: http://www.MaccabeeOnTheMantel.com